Meet Joe

Written by Amanda Cant
and Ruth Mezits

Illustrated by Liz McIntosh

D1448168

Joe got on his bike...

and went to town.

He saw Granny.

She said, "Slow down!"

Joe got on his bike...

and went to play.

He saw Annie.

She said, "Go away!"

Joe got on his bike...

and went to the lake.

He saw Ricky.

Ricky said, "Brake! Brake!"

Joe got on his bike...

and went too fast.

He saw Billy.

Billy said, "You're last!"

Joe got on his bike
And went to town.
He saw Granny.
She said, "Slow down!"

Joe got on his bike
And went to play.
He saw Annie.
She said, "Go away!"

Joe got on his bike
And went to the lake.
He saw Ricky.
Ricky said, "Brake! Brake!"

Joe got on his bike
And went too fast.
He saw Billy.
Billy said, "You're last!"